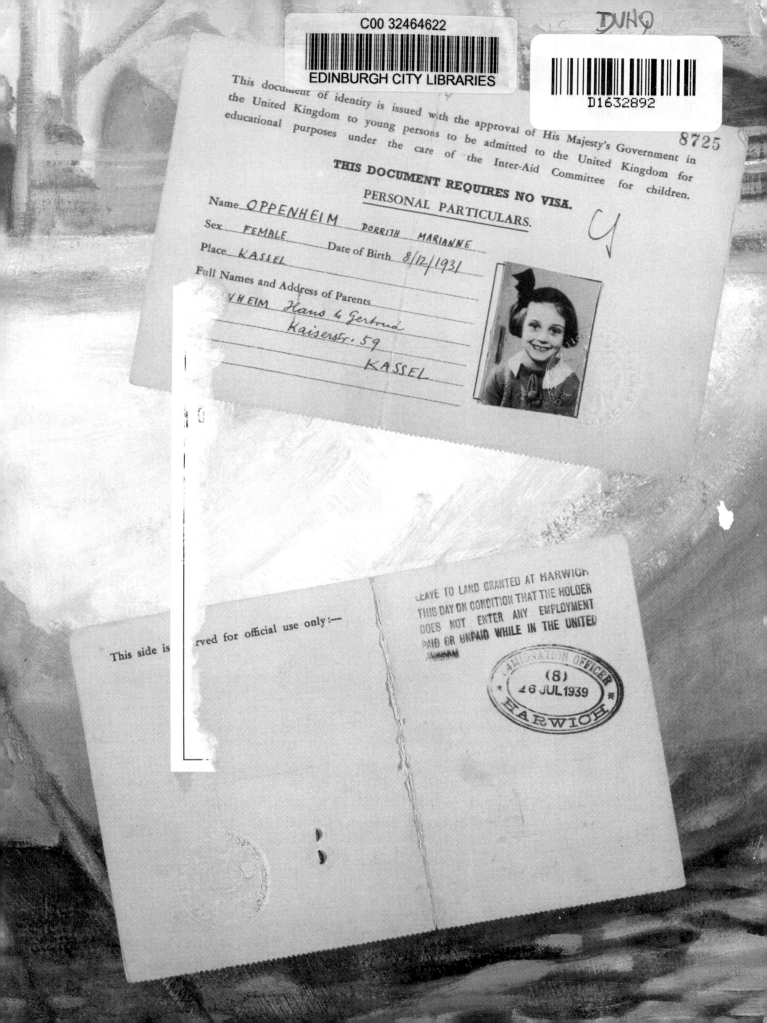

This document of identity is issued with the approval of His Majesty's Government in the United Kingdom to young persons to be admitted to the United Kingdom for educational purposes under the care of the Inter-Aid Committee for children.

**THIS DOCUMENT REQUIRES NO VISA.**

8725

## PERSONAL PARTICULARS.

Name OPPENHEIM DORRITH MARIANNE

Sex FEMALE          Date of Birth 8/12/1931

Place KASSEL

Full Names and Address of Parents

...HEIM Hans & Gertrud

Kaiserstr. 59

KASSEL

This side is ...rved for official use only :—

LEAVE TO LAND GRANTED AT HARWICH
THIS DAY ON CONDITION THAT THE HOLDER
DOES NOT ENTER ANY EMPLOYMENT
PAID OR UNPAID WHILE IN THE UNITED
...

IMMIGRATION OFFICER
(8)
26 JUL 1939
HARWICH

To Andrew, who gave me so much support
and for our children, grandchildren and great grandchildren    DMS

Thanks to Becky and Debbie    GF

"I was 7½ when my visa was stamped on 26 July, 1939.

There were almost 10,000 children like me, who came to the
United Kingdom before World War II began.  Some of us were
babies; most of us were Jewish.  We were each given a place
on a Kindertransport out of Nazi Europe.  After the War, some
of us were reunited with our families.  Sadly many of us were
not, and we either stayed in our new countries, where we grew
up, or went to live in different countries, all over the world."

Text copyright © 1996 Dorrith M. Sim
Illustrations copyright © 1996 Gerald Fitzgerald

The author hereby asserts her moral right to
be identified as the author of this work.

ISBN 978-0-948785-05-4

Published 2012 by J.R. Reid
Printed and bound by Exacta Print Ltd, Glasgow

Distributed by Exacta Print Ltd
92-96 West Regent Street, Glasgow G2 2QD, Scotland
Tel: +44 (0)141 352 6800
Email: sales@exactaprint.com
Website: www.exactaprint.com

# In My Pocket

By Dorrith M. Sim
Illustrated by Gerald Fitzgerald

Hardly anyone on the boat
   ate breakfast that morning.

It was 1939.
It was July.
And we were on a boat.
A boat full of children
   escaping from danger.

Back at the Hamburg train station,
  a train had been waiting.
Waiting to take us to Holland,
  to the boat.
      Mutti and Vati told me the boat
       would take us to a new life.
        All the parents cried.
        We cried, too.

One little girl cried loudest of all,
    when she dropped her toy dog.
It lay on the tracks.
A man rescued the dog.
He called, "Catch!" as he threw it to her.
Right after she caught it, the train began to move.
The girl stopped crying and clutched her dog.
And she waved goodbye to the man.

At last, the train stopped.
A big boy said we were in Holland.
We sat in a green field and ate
cheese sandwiches.

We sang songs to the Dutch people
   who helped us.
One song was about a mermaid.
They gave us milk and chocolate.
Soon we were on our way again.

On the boat, it was strange sleeping
    without our parents.
Only brothers and sisters knew anyone.
In the night, some children got lost.
They left their cabins to look for the bathrooms,
    and could not remember their way back.

Then it was time to leave the boat.
We wore name tags around our necks.
There was a wooden bridge.
Looking through the slats at the sea
 made me dizzy.
I didn't want to move but everyone
 behind pushed me.
I shut my eyes and held the rail.
I shuffled forward with my eyes closed.
At last, my feet touched the ground.
That's when I started to cry.

A train stood ready.
Someone said it was a British
    train, taking us to London.
Many people were there.
Some children had friends or
    family to meet them.
Others looked around for help.
There were men with cameras,
    and people holding photographs.
Those people had promised to take
    children into their homes.
The children would be part of
    their families until they could be
    with their own parents again.

A man and a woman looked
   at a photograph.
The wife touched her husband's arm.
"Look," she said. "The child we
   picked. The girl with the red
   ribbon and the big toy dog."
That's how they found me.

A man with them spoke German.
He said, "Willkommen schön Kind."
All I could say in English was,
   "I have a handkerchief in my pocket."
That's how I began to teach myself.
Whenever I learned a new word,
   I put it in the same sentence.
"I have a dog in my pocket.
I have a house in my pocket.
I have a teacher in my pocket."

The man and woman came from Scotland.
Everything there was different.
In Germany, I sat on a little seat on my father's bike.
In Edinburgh, where they lived, there was a car.
And I had a real dog.

In Germany, I couldn't play with
the children in our street,
because I was Jewish.
Now I played with my new
Scottish friends.
Soon I was calling the woman
and man Mummy and Daddy.
After all, I called my real
parents Mutti and Vati.

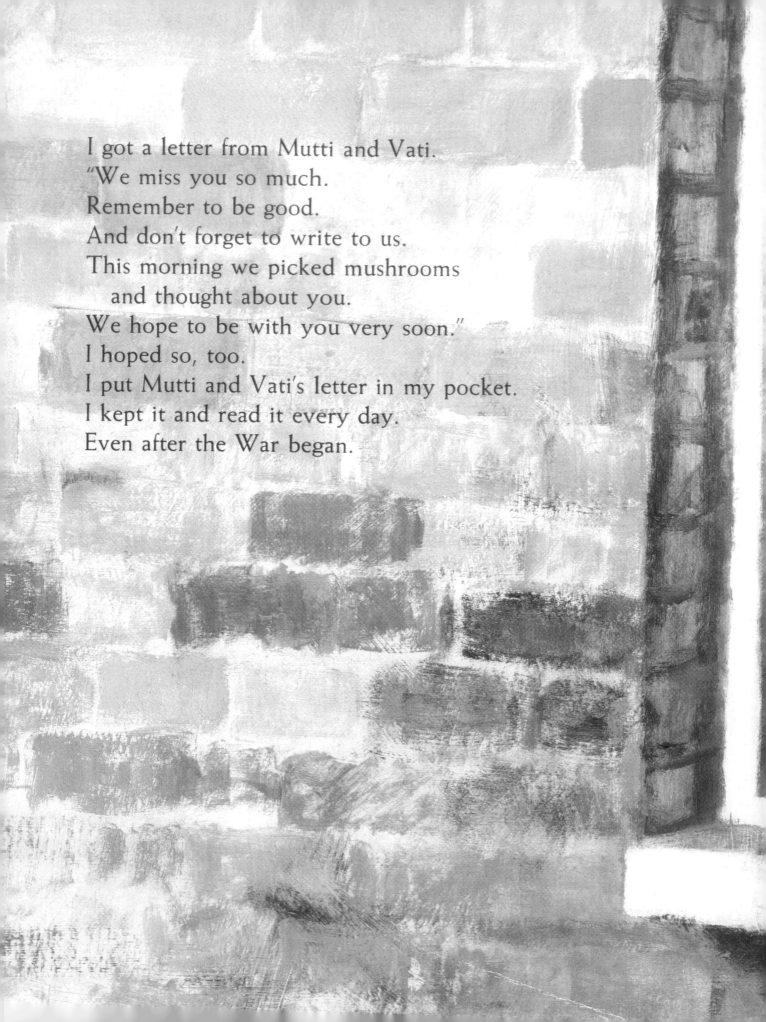

I got a letter from Mutti and Vati.
"We miss you so much.
Remember to be good.
And don't forget to write to us.
This morning we picked mushrooms
   and thought about you.
We hope to be with you very soon."
I hoped so, too.
I put Mutti and Vati's letter in my pocket.
I kept it and read it every day.
Even after the War began.